Even More Parts

Even More Parts

Even More Parts

IDIOMS FROM HEAD TO TOE

Quit messing with my head!

Tedd Arnold

SCHOLASTIC INC.

New York Toronto London Auckland Sydney
Mexico City New Delhi Hong Kong Buenos Aires

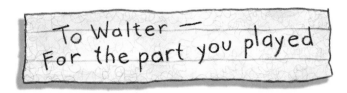

To Walter —
For the part you played

ISBN 0-439-80361-6

12 11 10 9 8 7 6 5 4 3 2 1   5 6 7 8 9 10/0

Printed in the U.S.A.   40

First Scholastic printing, September 2005

Typography by Nancy R. Leo-Kelly

The art was prepared using color pencils and watercolor washes,
and the text was hand-lettered by the artist.

Sometimes I wish my stupid ears
Weren't always open wide.
They hear such strange and crazy talk—
I'm scared to go outside!

I jotted down a list of all
The scary things I've heard.
Believe me, all of these are real.
I wrote them word for word.

To leave my bedroom unprepared,
I'd have to be a fool!
Excuse me now. There's work to do
Before I go to school.

My eyes are glued to the television.

There are so many **crazy** things
I have to keep in mind!
I sure don't want to accidentally
Leave my parts behind.

Mom says, "Dear, it's time for school.
Let's go or you'll be late."
Then Dad says, "Just remember, son...